www.raintreepublishers.co.uk

Visit our website to find out more information about Raintree books.

To order:

☎ Phone 0845 6044371
🖨 Fax +44 (0) 1865 312263
✉ Email myorders@raintreepublishers.co.uk

Customers from outside the UK please telephone +44 1865 312262

Raintree is an imprint of Capstone Global Library Limited, a company incorporated in England and Wales having its registered office at 7 Pilgrim Street, London, EC4V 6LB - Registered company number: 6695582

First published by Raintree in 2013
The moral rights of the proprietor have been asserted.

Originally published by DC Comics in the U.S. in single magazine form as Batman Adventures #1.
Copyright © 2012 DC Comics. All Rights Reserved.

STONE ARCH BOOKS
Ashley C. Andersen Zantop *Publisher*
Michael Dahl *Editorial Director*
Donald Lemke & Sean Tulien *Editors*
Heather Kindseth *Creative Director*
Bob Lentz *Designer*
Kathy McColley *Production Specialist*
Printed and bound in China.

DC COMICS
Joan Hilty *Original U.S. Editor*
Harvey Richards *U.S. Assistant Editor*
Bruce Timm *Cover Artist*

ISBN 978 1 406 25408 2
16 15 14 13
10 9 8 7 6 5 4 3 2

British Library Cataloguing in Publication Data
A full catalogue record for this book is available from the British Library.

BATMAN ADVENTURES

NO ASYLUM

Ty Templeton & Dan Slott......................writers
Rick Burchett & Ty Templeton ....pencillers
Terry Beatty .... inker
Lee Loughridge .... colorist
Phil Felix ....letterer

**Batman created by
Bob Kane**

WHAT'S *THAT?* THE *UMBRELLA SIGNAL?*

IT'S NOT ENOUGH HE GOT ELECTED *MAYOR?* COBBLEPOT WANTS TO BE THE *SUPER-HERO* NOW?

COBBLEPOT for MAYOR
LAW and ORDER...
FOR A CHANGE

COMPUTER.

DIAL COMMISSIONER GORDON'S OFFICE.

HELLO?

LOOKS LIKE PENGUIN IS KEEPING HIS CAMPAIGN PROMISE ABOUT ME...

I'VE GOT A BLACK-AND-WHITE ON MY TAIL.

UNIT 5607. OFFICER SPERLING, ISN'T IT?

HE'S NOT MUCH OF A DRIVER...

...I DON'T WANT HIM TO GET HURT.

I...

I CAN'T DO ANYTHING ABOUT IT, BATMAN.

OUR *NEW MAYOR* MADE IT CLEAR HE CONSIDERED YOU AN *OUTLAW* ON THE DAY HE WAS SWORN INTO OFFICE.

SCREECH!

UH-HUH. SO WHY LIGHT THE SIGNAL?

IT'S ARKHAM ASYLUM...

EVERY ALARM'S GONE OFF UP THERE. PHONES AND SECURITY CAMERAS ARE DOWN.

WHATEVER PROBLEMS IT CAUSES ME, YOUR PRESENCE WILL SAVE LIVES...

I'M ALREADY ON MY WAY TO ARKHAM.

WHAT...? I ONLY FOUND OUT A MOMENT AGO MYSELF...

I HAVE MY *OWN* PERIMETER ALARM UP THERE.

AND SOME ACCESS TO THEIR SECURITY SYSTEM--

--SUCH AS IT IS.

ARKHAM ASYLUM IS A *FEDERAL FACILITY*, BATMAN...

YOU *SHOULDN'T* HAVE DONE THAT. YOU WANT *THOSE* PEOPLE AFTER YOU TOO?

THEY SHOULDN'T LOSE SO MANY INMATES.

GIVE ME TEN MINUTES BEFORE YOU SEND YOUR MEN IN, JIM.

BUT--

TEN MINUTES. I HAVE TO GO.

SCREECH!

WOOSH!

7

YOU THREE! COME WITH US!

W- WHAT...?

NO!

YOU ARE THE SAFE ONES. GET THE INNOCENTS FAR FROM THIS FLOOR, BROTHER!

IVY!

KRAK!

DO NOT HARM HARLEY QUINN.

TWO-FACE... IS TO BE SECOND.

WE THOUGHT HE MIGHT LIKE THAT...

STOP!

YOU DON'T DECIDE IF I LIVE OR DIE...

THAT'S UP TO THE COIN.

HM. JUST MY LUCK.

ALL RIGHT. NOW YOU CAN COME AT ME.

THESE MEN ARE *ASSASSINS* IN THE *SOCIETY OF SHADOWS.*

THEY WORK FOR A MAN NAMED *RA'S AL GHUL.*

WHAT ARE THEY DOING HERE? WHO'S MADE AN ENEMY OF THIS MAN?

WHY DO *YOU* GET TO ASK ALL THE QUESTIONS?

uhhh... I DON'T KNOW ABOUT HARVEY...

...BUT *I'VE* NEVER HEARD OF THIS *GHOUL* FELLA...AND I DON'T KNOW WHAT HE'S GOT AGAINST *ME.*

IVY!

YOU'RE ALIVE!

NO KIDDING.

YOU'RE NOT EVEN *BLEED-ING!*

WE ALL *SAW* THE SWORD GO THROUGH YA! HOW--?

WE HAVE *BIGGER* PROBLEMS NOW, HARL.

YOU KEEPING SECRETS FROM *ME* IS A PRETTY BIG PROBLEM!

SCARE-CROW...

...YOU ARE *NEXT!*

14

ARE YOU ALL RIGHT?

YES... TWO OF 'EM RAN PAST... *THAT* WAY.

JUST *NOW*.

‹LOOK! BATMAN... IN THE POLICE SEARCHLIGHT!›

‹WE MUST LEAVE!›

WHOOOSH!

I'M GOING TO NEED A PICKUP AT LOCATION *KING BAKER SEVEN* IN TEN MINUTES.

OF COURSE. WAS YOUR EVENING "ENCOURAGING" AFTER ALL, SIR?

...THANKS TO SOME *BAD TIMING* WITH THE POLICE.

PEOPLE GOT AWAY FROM ME.

FOR *NOW.*

ALFRED.

SIR...?

NOT SO FAR...

NEXT: **WHERE IS THE RIDDLER?!?**

WHO AM I?

DAN SLOTT--WRITER TY TEMPLETON--PENCILLER
TERRY BEATTY--INKER LEE LOUGHRIDGE--COLORIST
PHIL FELIX--LETTERER
HARVEY RICHARDS--ASSISTANT EDITOR
JOAN HILTY--EDITOR

THAT MOMENT OF TRAGEDY PUT ME ON THE PATH TO WHAT I'VE *BECOME.*

THE *PROMISE* I MADE.

THE YEARS OF *STUDY...*

...HONING *MIND* AND *BODY.*

WAITING FOR A *SIGN...*

...A WAY TO *TAKE BACK* THE NIGHT.

24

HEY, *CAVALIER!* IN *HERE,* MAN!

WE GOT YOUR BACK, *C!*

3

WEEEOOO

AND ONCE AGAIN, THE CAVALIER *SLIPS AWAY...*

... THANKS TO HIS *ADORING PUBLIC!*

THAT'S QUITE A *SCAM* YOU'VE GOT!

BATMAN!

...AND KEEPING MOST FOR *YOURSELF!*

YOUR *PAYOFFS* MAY *ENDEAR* YOU TO THE *STREET SCUM* OF GOTHAM--

WAK!

--BUT NOT TO *ME.*

YOU'RE NOTHING MORE THAN A COMMON THIEF.

ROBBING FROM THE RICH, GIVING TO THE POOR...

CREATORS

TY TEMPLETON WRITER & PENCILLER

Ty Templeton was born in the wilds of downtown Toronto, Canada to a show-business family. He makes his living writing and drawing comic books, working on such characters as Batman, Superman, Spider-Man, The Simpsons, the Avengers, and many others.

DAN SLOTT WRITER

Dan Slott is a comics writer best known for his work on DC Comics' *Arkham Asylum*, and, for Marvel, *The Avengers* and the *Amazing Spider-Man*.

RICK BURCHETT PENCILLER

Rick Burchett has worked as a comics artist for more than 25 years. He has received the comics industry's Eisner Award three times, Spain's Haxtur Award, and he has been nominated for the Eagle Award. Rick lives with his wife and two sons in Missouri, USA.

TERRY BEATTY INKER

For more than ten years, Terry Beatty was the main inker of DC Comics' "animated-style" Batman comics, including *The Batman Strikes*. More recently, he worked on *Return to Perdition*, a graphic novel for DC's Vertigo Crime.

GLOSSARY

assassin person who kills another person, often for money

campaign connected series of activities designed to bring about a particular result, such as winning an election

commissioner official in charge of a government department, such as the police department

gruesome causing horror or disgust

honing making more intense or effective

liability something that works as a disadvantage

neutralized made ineffective

outlaw criminal, especially one who is running away from the law

pathetic causing one to feel tenderness, pity, or sorrow

perimeter boundary of an area

stealth intended not to attract attention

tragedy very sad event

vigilante member of a group of volunteers who decide to stop crime and punish criminals

BATMAN GLOSSARY

Alfred Pennyworth: Bruce Wayne's loyal butler. He knows Bruce Wayne's secret identity and helps the Dark Knight solve crimes in Gotham City.

Arkham Asylum: a psychiatric hospital in Gotham City that often holds the world's most dangerous and insane criminals, such as the Joker, Scarecrow, Two-Face, and Scarface.

Bat-Signal: a distress signal used by the Gotham City Police Department to notify the Dark Knight of danger or their need for his help.

Batarang: a metal, bat-shaped weapon that can be thrown like a boomerang.

Commissioner James Gordon: head of the Gotham City Police Department and a loyal friend of the Dark Knight.

Oswald Cobblepot: sometimes the mayor of Gotham City, but always known to Batman as the Penguin, a mastermind of the city's criminal underworld.

Society of Shadows: an organization of highly trained assassins led by Ra's al Ghul, a centuries-old assassin who hopes to rid the world of humanity.

Two-Face: after having his face disfigured, Harvey Dent, the city's former district attorney, turned to a life of crime, basing life or death decisions on the flip of a coin.

VISUAL QUESTIONS & PROMPTS

1. The way a character's eyes and mouth look, also known as their facial expression, can tell a lot about the emotions he or she is feeling. In the image on the right, how do you think the Dark Knight is feeling? Use the illustration to explain your answer.

2. The Dark Knight often uses high-tech devices while solving crimes, including flying weapons called Batarangs (see panel below). Identify two other panels in which Batman uses one of his high-tech gadgets. Describe them and write about how these devices could be useful in fighting crime.

--BUT NOT TO ME.

YOU'RE NOTHING MORE THAN A COMMON THIEF.

1

WHOK

2

3. The Dark Knight is an expert martial artist. Find at least two panels in this book where Batman uses this skill. Do you believe he could've solved those problems differently? Why or why not?

...HONING *MIND* AND *BODY.*

3

4 Several of Batman's worst enemies appear in this book, including the Joker, Scarface, Killer Croc, Poison Ivy, and Two-Face. In the panel below, why do you think Two-Face chose to help Batman instead of hurt him?

5 The Dark Knight fights to rid the city of crime. At the end of the story, why do you think Batman chose to destroy the police department's Bat-Signal? Explain your answer using examples from the story.

BATMAN ADVENTURES

Raintree